THROUGH
THEIR EYES

WAR OF WORDS

Edited By Kat Cockrill

First published in Great Britain in 2020 by:

Young Writers
Remus House
Coltsfoot Drive
Peterborough
PE2 9BF
Telephone: 01733 890066
Website: www.youngwriters.co.uk

Printed and bound in the UK by BookPrintingUK
Website: www.bookprintinguk.com
YB0433P

FOREWORD

Since 1991, here at Young Writers we have celebrated the awesome power of creative writing, especially in young adults, where it can serve as a vital method of expressing strong (and sometimes difficult) emotions, a conduit to develop empathy, and a safe, non-judgemental place to explore one's own place in the world. With every poem we see the effort and thought that each pupil published in this book has put into their work and by creating this anthology we hope to encourage them further with the ultimate goal of sparking a life-long love of writing.

Through Their Eyes challenged young writers to open their minds and pen bold, powerful poems from the points-of-view of any person or concept they could imagine – from celebrities and politicians to animals and inanimate objects, or even just to give us a glimpse of the world as they experience it. The result is this fierce collection of poetry that by turns questions injustice, imagines the innermost thoughts of influential figures or simply has fun.

The nature of the topic means that contentious or controversial figures may have been chosen as the narrators, and as such some poems may contain views or thoughts that, although may represent those of the person being written about, by no means reflect the opinions or feelings of either the author or us here at Young Writers.

We encourage young writers to express themselves and address subjects that matter to them, which sometimes means writing about sensitive or difficult topics. If you have been affected by any issues raised in this book, details on where to find help can be found at *www.youngwriters.co.uk/info/other/contact-lines*

CONTENTS

Georgie McLenaghan (15)	70
Susan Green (15)	71
Marshall Neill (16)	72
Rachel McCollum (14)	73
Ella Stewart (14)	74
Luke Walton (14)	75
Harry Hunter Hughes (15)	76
Evie Scott (13)	77
Charlie Orr (14)	78
Charlotte Lynn (15)	79
Natasha Hamilton (14)	80
Toby McAuley (13)	81
Kenzi Glass (16)	82

Smestow School, Castlecroft

Deimante Jonikaviciute (12)	83
Abigail Bate (12)	84
Amelia Shokar (12)	85
Ella Smith (12)	86

The Wigston Academies Trust, Wigston

Natasha Taylor (12)	87
Cameron Lee (12)	88
Harsimran Sadhra (12)	90
Freya Mistry (13)	92
Alyssa Eve Vaja (12)	93
Marissa Faye McFarlane (12)	94
Raegan Hamp (12)	96
Lottie Parnham (12)	97
Lukas Peikstenis (11)	98
Myah Seager (11)	99
Ashleigh Silver (11)	100
Mia Jennifer Berry (11)	101
Theo Thomas Burrows (11)	102
Lily-Mae Jobling (12)	103
Georgia Sylvester (12)	104
Jamie Lakin (13)	105
Daniel Craven (11)	106
Alex Exton (12)	107
Emily Crouch (13) & Molly Hanney (13)	108

Cassie Birdas (11)	109
Lili Rutter (12)	110
Mason Johnson (12)	111
Sara Filali (12)	112
Faye Chloe Hincks (13)	113
Milly Jade Shaw (12)	114
Frances Mitchell (12)	115
Woody Orton (12)	116
Danny Beattie (12)	117
Oliver Bailey (12)	118
Anya Brown (11)	119
Hannah Vann (12)	120

Walney School, Walney

Tyler Anthony Shannon (11)	121
Phoebe Lovidge (14)	122
Neve Fallon (14)	123

THE
POEMS

Within These Plastic Walls

As I strut through the doors with a flourish,
I see all the eyes look my way, stares boring into the back of
my skull,
Hair curled, lips pouting, hips swaying,
I greet my accomplices and find my way through yet
another school day,
My worshippers separating to pave my way.

But, behind the mask of confidence and beauty
Is a girl hidden within the plastic walls of her delusional
mind,
A picture of pure innocence and desperation,
Pleading and begging to be freed of her entrapment,
Pressure, judged, eager to please,
Concealing her feelings yet falling to her knees.

But, as I feel her cries within my chest,
A pain awakens, clutching me tight,
For a second, I become the one I fear,
content on concealing her throughout day and night.

But, I push her down, down deep inside,
Gifting her a special place to hide,
A special place hidden within these plastic walls,
To be concealed no matter how loud she calls.

Aimee Jackson (13)
Altrincham College Of Arts, Timperley

Not Perfect World

This country will never exist,
This country's lost in the world's dark,
But, let me just assist you to see
How perfect it could be.

Imagine a country with no war
And only peace around,
No poorness, litter, hate or crime,
Everyone is happy and alive.

My name is Lucky, I'm a dog,
A black Labrador more precisely,
My soul is not as black as my hairs,
Vice versa, it's as bright as the sun.

My owner is a kind man with a beard,
He never makes me sad,
But once he put me out in the field,
I never was as mad.

I wondered for a long time,
I couldn't get it clear,
The one to whom I was dependent,
Changed me to nothing dear.

Nice family from very far
Brought me to their house,
It was so big, like from my dream,
But I missed the old one still.

The years went past,
The country went down,
Poverty, litter, hate and crime,
It all existed now.

It couldn't stay the same,
At one moment, we had all changed,
The country split into two sides,
One is perfect and one is blind.

Blind because they don't want to see
How bad they are,
How people live.

I live on the rich side
But do I want it?
No, the answer is right.

I 'took' my paws,
I ran as fast as ever,
I felt that I had to come back
To my native land, my heart was whispering.

Two sides started to fight,
So many people died,
All had been changed,
Now it seems like real life.

Daryna Siardziuk (12)
Altrincham College Of Arts, Timperley

The Truth About The Man On TV

I heard him on TV,
Bragging about how we can change this country for the better,
His crooked tongue shouting obscenities and false hope,
Politics and perfection is the topic at every family's dinner table,
Climate change is upon us and everything so pure and lush is dying,
Hear the animal kingdom crying but the man on TV is lying,
Our youth has been infected by everything foul and cruel,
Mental health rises and the youth are given false solutions and tactics,
The man on TV and the elite capitalise our problems,
Our world is a money-making machine,
We are all dragging our society into the streets
Even without knowing so,
We are all living in fear of what's to come,
We are so fearful, we can't even turn to our brothers and sisters any more,
Fearing that our neighbours, partners, workers and children
Are backstabbing soul-takers,
We fear the people who are just like us
But we dehumanise and stereotype these people,
Arabs and Muslims with bombs in their pockets and signals of the Taliban,
Black people with their voodoo and steel daggers, ready to curse and attack,

Teenagers in gangs with knives up their sleeves,
Ready for their murder call as they come across an innocent soul,
We turn for hope to our youth and to the unique ones in the pack,
Ready to attack and shove our problems down their throats,
Assimilating them into obscurity,
The man on TV despises us all,
It's our future, the time to strike is now, "Heal the world, make it a better place."

Beatrice Gonzalez-Dearden (14)
Altrincham College Of Arts, Timperley

A Name Defines A Person

Money for charity we try to give
But, from us, will they take it? No!
Being banned from helping people hurts,
But we can't change the past so we go,
'Cause in their eyes, a name defines a person.

Another one comes to stir more trouble,
Adding some rumours to tell the 'truth',
Affecting an old man's past
And a child's youth,
Fixing it will be a difficult task,
But they won't back down,
No matter how hard they ask,
'Cause, in their minds, a name defines a person.

In one call, they'll all come down,
Lighting the world with red and blue,
He stands still, helping someone out,
Even though he knew
In their law, a name defines a person.

Years ago, a bad thing happened,
Leaving future generations trapped,
Old generations trying to fix things,
But, they're not allowed and that's a fact,
Thanks to a few people,
In everyone's hearts, a name defines a person.

Now, years later, I sit,
I sit, only just learning about a past,
One that I had nothing, but still so much, to do with,
Questions are being asked, so I have to think fast.

I lie, I lie to my friends,
To people I care about the most,
I guess it's not really a lie
But not our story, our history,
'Cause, deep down, it's just like everyone else,
Deep down, I believe
A name defines a person.

Lily-May Fox-Noonan (13)
Altrincham College Of Arts, Timperley

Jesy Nelson: Odd One Out

My dream of being a singer has finally come true,
Then I receive a message from you,
Of course, you come after me, dragging me down,
Ruining this moment, making me frown,
All I try and do is impress people,
But your poison words are proven lethal,
Singing and dancing is my absolute passion,
Why do they care about my weight and fashion?
"You're fat, you're ugly." Oh, not this again,
What did I do to deserve this, tell me when?
Oh, why can't I be like them?

Text after text, please can it end?
All I need is to tell someone how I'm feeling, like a friend,
All I really want is the pain to go away,
I need to change fast, I'll do it today,
From now on, I'll be at my best,
I will put myself to my absolute test,
I have to look good
Otherwise, there'll be bad comments
Coming my way like a flood,
Lipstick, eyeshadow, I hope I look good.

I miss the old Jesy,
But I don't like that time, it was all messy,
By far, that was the worst time of my life,
Every day it stabs my heart like a knife,

To this very day, I'm still scared
Of the comments I'll get, but I'm prepared,
My friends and family, we form a pack,
But self-confidence I lack,
The old Jesy has made me who I am today,
If you're in a situation like me, speak,
You will get through this.

Darcy Heaton (11)

Altrincham College Of Arts, Timperley

I See The Glory

I get passed the ball
From the right-winger
But that same day,
He made fun of me being ginger.

I looked up to the same guy
But, instead, I cried deep inside,
I hit the ball but it goes wide,
Later that day, my face got pied.

After the game, in the lockers,
I got knocked around by the blockers,
I walk home with cuts and bruises,
The next day, I'm the one he chooses.

Two people approach me in the dark,
I'm standing alone in a park,
I clench my fists as we look eye to eye,
I'm feeling that one of us is about to die.

In the toilets, they approach me again,
I'm feeling sick, I punch one of them in the head,
One of them is down, he's going to bed,
The only thing I see on the floor is red.

I look up all I see is top right,
The same guy is shouting at me from the other side,
I curve the ball, I see how it flies,
I get scouted but my sexuality is denied.

I protest my sexuality,
But they won't accept it as it's a fatality,
I get called names, "Gay!" "Queer!" "Bent!"
In my heart, there's a dent.

I've been knocked down, but I look up,
I really want it, I want that gold cup,
I fight hard so they bring back up,
Eventually, I build up, I see the glory.

Alexander William Lee Anthony (13) & Louis

Altrincham College Of Arts, Timperley

They Are All The Same

I see people all around,
All different heights and sizes,
But, all of them are the same,
All of them have a part of them
That has the need to feel powerful,
So, they pick on the weaker kids,
The ones who can't fend for themselves,
The satisfaction of feeling big,
The feeling of being superior,
It takes over.

So, they carry on,
They pick on the weak kids every day,
Each victim making them feel more powerful,
They are weak,
They are stupid,
All said for what?
A stupid feeling.

Blink and they are there,
Dream and they are there,
I see them wherever I go,
I wonder how it feels
To be the bigger kid,
To be the one who is strong,
I wonder if they know
How I feel.

Honestly, I feel bad for them,
They have to make someone else feel bad
So they can feel good,
I'm always happy doing what I like,
So my mum told me to carry on,
"If they bully you one more time,
Tell me,"
So, I go to school,
I hear that there is a new kid,
Someone from Saudi Arabia,
I go home,
Something catches my eye,
Blink and they are there,
Dream and they are there,
They are all the same.

Michael Davidson-Chen (13)

Altrincham College Of Arts, Timperley

Inbound

Scramble, scramble, scramble,
The war raged on,
Thunder and clouds,
Fighters inbound.

Cleared for take-off,
Not knowing my fate,
Thunder and clouds,
Fighters inbound.

In the air now
And stretching for miles,
A greeny-blue, translucent sea,
Thunder and clouds,
Fighters inbound.

I put the file away
As we're a mile away,
Getting ready for combat,
Would this be the last time?
Thunder and clouds,
Fighters inbound.

Bang! Bang! Bang!
"Shots fired!" I yelled,
We all dispersed,
Not knowing where he was,
Blinded by the sun,

Thunder and lightning,
We're under attack.

In formation again,
Ten dots on the radar,
We're no match for them,
Thunder and lightning,
We're under attack.

Head to head again,
Everyone opened fire,
Nine dots on the radar,
Thunder and lightning,
We're under attack.

It was like gangs in a shoot out,
Only, in mid-air,
We all know only one side could win,
Thunder and lightning,
We're under attack.

Alex McManus (14)
Altrincham College Of Arts, Timperley

Truth

The truth is, truth hurts.
They say what hurts makes you stronger,
but it doesn't feel that way.
People sleep on streets and we pay no notice.
We walk by and leave them freezing
and, the fact is, we don't give a damn.

The truth is racism exists.
And black people are hurt because of
the colour of their skin.
As if insulting and assaulting
is going to change the world.

The fact is homophobia is a thing.
What is the point of judging people
on their sexuality or gender,
"That's gay!" as some people say.
But is that meant to be wrong?
So what if people are gay or bisexual or lesbian?
Why don't we stop judging people on their sexuality
and just accept that they are people like you and I?

I wonder, why do people go to war?
We fight over stupid reasons such as race, religion or
ethnicity.
In America, people carry guns as easily as a bag.
What is wrong with some people?
It's not just guns, knives too.

The truth is the truth hurts
And what hurts makes us stronger.

Jay Brown (13)
Altrincham College Of Arts, Timperley

Mankind Knows What Mankind Knows

They've ruined it,
He gave them every chance but they ruined it.

He watched them guzzle his vital fuel,
The fuel that keeps him at bay,
The fuel that fuels his content emotion
But they stand too close in his way.

But, 'the man' says no,
'The man' refuses to believe he exists,
Yet, 'the man, still guzzles the fuel, the vital fuel,
The fuel that keeps him at bay.

And, his blood continues to boil,
Boil until boils on his body begin to burst,
Filled with plastic bottles and bags and broken glass,
While mankind sit and watch as his cheeks strike with fire,
Raging fire,
Fire that eats its way though forests, trees and wildlife.

But, mankind knows what mankind knows,
It knows that the innocent whale, or tiger, or tree
Is no the purpose of his actions,
Because mankind knows what mankind knows
And his actions are placed in the hands of mankind.

Millie Hampson-May (13)
Altrincham College Of Arts, Timperley

A Prisoner Of War

A bandoned castles and houses lock-up this hell we're in,

P risoners killed every day, *could I be next?* I wonder each day,

R eal people turned to monsters by one man they all obey,

I mages of my loved ones fill my head,

S ons of men I never knew died for me, now I die for you,

O rion's belt might be the last thing I see,

N ew prisoners come every day, we try to warn but they disobey,

E arly one day, my name gets called,

R eady to die for my country, I clean myself up,

O ff we go to the firing squad... *bang!* I'm dead,

F ires burn, burning all the dead.

W omen and children hear the news

A nd break down in tears and scream away their blues,

R eady to take revenge for the lovers they have lost.

Stephanie Jones (13)
Altrincham College Of Arts, Timperley

Attacked

It's fun,
Isn't it
Being made out as dumb
And believing it's true.
So, now, they feel blue,
Being attacked not just by their minds,
But maybe by you.
I mean, why make them feel good?
I don't think you have kindness in your heart
Because, people like you, you're animals,
You have a thirst for blood,
A craving for flesh,
Maybe even something fresh?
Why?
Why bully people?
Why harass them?
Make them feel lonely
So, now, they hide in a den
Made in their head
As they hide from the bad.
Great! They're scared,
I hope you're not feeling glad,
You torture their minds,
Make them feel lost in a maze
Of lies and insults of all kinds,
Stop bullying people, this isn't a race

To see who first
Can put a frown on a face...

Emma Sarah Tighe (13)
Altrincham College Of Arts, Timperley

This Is My Reality

- Through a turtle's eyes -

How would you feel
If your home got destroyed?
How would you feel
If you watched your best friend
Getting dragged away by a fishing net?
How would you feel
If the place you were born
Was filled by mountains of litter?
This is my reality.

What would you do
If you saw your family,
Floating dead in front of you?
What would you do if
You watched masses of your siblings
Run to the city instead of the sea?
What would you do if the place your eggs were laid
Was submerged in water?
This is my reality.

How would you feel
If your world was drained of its colour?
How would you feel if the food you ate
Poisoned you?
How would you feel if your species

Was on the edge of extinction?
This is my reality.

Leah Manders-Ratcliff (13) & Amelie Ide (13)

Altrincham College Of Arts, Timperley

The Mind Of A Bully

He drinks and he drinks
And he just won't stop,
His life in my hands and I'm only thirteen.

My siblings are small,
Only five and ten,
I take them to school every day,
I make them dinner every night,
It's the same thing over and over.

But, yet, I've never
Blown out the candles on a cake,
I've never had a proper Christmas dinner.

My home is cold,
Dark,
Small
And covered in mould,
We all share a room
Smaller than the bathroom in Costa.

I have no friends
And my mother is gone,
I'm all alone, with no shoulder to cry on.

"I'm scared," I say,
Scared of the hatred filled up inside,
I just want to run but I'm stuck,
Stuck here with the bully I call my father.

Poppy Green
Altrincham College Of Arts, Timperley

My Kingdom

When I look into my kingdom,
There are majestic tigers,
There are powerful gorillas,
There are sneaky panthers
But, slowly, my kingdom is fading away.

When I look into my kingdom,
There are brutal hunters,
There are no innocent lives,
There's red blood on the ground,
But, I'll show no mercy towards these ruthless hunters.

My jungle is thriving, when the humans aren't here,
It tastes like freedom,
It smells like life,
It sounds like innocent lives cheering,
It feels like victory,
It looks like heaven.

I am a king,
Not a slave,
I can rule.
My life is an extravagant story,
Animals alike
Love me.

Arnav Gupta (13)
Altrincham College Of Arts, Timperley

Trapped

I'm just not myself anymore,
Constantly afraid,
Constantly alone,
I need to get out
But it's not that easy.

I want to fight back
Against a big, strong man,
It just won't work,
I don't have a chance.

My body feels violated,
Aches and pains all over,
Each bruise a different colour,
I feel there's no way out.

There are still parts of me that love him,
But does he love me?
I really don't know,
I hope so.

I'm always scared
Of what he's going to do next,
Every corner I turn, he's there,
There's no way out.

I'm just not myself anymore,
Constantly afraid,

Constantly alone,
I need to get out,
But it's not that easy.

Abbie Cook (13)
Altrincham College Of Arts, Timperley

Nightmare

A mirror is my nightmare,
Continuously staring after every last meal,
Why can't I look like Victoria's Secret models?
Why can't I wear a bikini in public?
Why can't I be naturally skinny like other girls?
Zero posts on Instagram,
Hardly ever post on Snapchat,
Why do people stare at me if I wear a short top?
I want people to look at me and think,
Wow, look at her figure!

Social media is my nightmare,
Continuously staring, scrolling,
Why can't I stop?
Why do I have to know what everyone's doing twenty-four-
seven,
I have other things to do with my life,
Why do I only care about a number?

What's wrong with me?

Phoebe Whitehead (13)
Altrincham College Of Arts, Timperley

Who Am I? Who Am I Supposed To Be?

Who am I?
Who am I supposed to be?
Am I just a happy little girl you see?
I have a future like everyone else in the world,
But, social media will stop me,
Our world is quickly changing
And will start to change me,
But, will it change my image and happiness that everyone sees?
I'm living the 'gram like everyone else,
They love it but it stops me from loving myself,
My self-love is disappearing like a rhino going extinct,
Why does this world want everything ugly to be hidden?
Can you hear my voice through the filters and boomerangs?
Repeatedly asking for help,
But the likes you give me are just sticky plasters
Hiding all my deep feelings.

Sophia Rose Ooi (14)
Altrincham College Of Arts, Timperley

Change

We all stand in the street,
Stomping our feet to the beat,
As we shout to the crowd,
Our message very, very loud.

But, that guy at number ten
Is hiding out in his den,
Too busy with Brexit
As he is trying to exit.

There's also that big, orange snake
That says, "It's all fake
Made up by the Chinese
To make the world beg on its knees!"

But I know the truth,
We all know the truth,
That sea levels are rising
And that the world is dying.

That the ice is melting
Because we are polluting,
If we don't do something now,
We will have to bow down.

Nils van Dongen (13)
Altrincham College Of Arts, Timperley

Always Another Side To The Story...

Anxiety, depression, the sleepless nights,
Asking for help can't be right,
Scared to death, scared for my life,
Jumping to conclusions, jumping to the knife,
Scars on my arm showing my life like a map,
Looking at them reliving every moment,
When I see them, my shadow self pops out like an app,
Bipolar disorder like a drug,
Saying medication will help,
It doesn't, making me itch like a bug.

Walk into school, nobody knows what I have done,
Covering my arms, pretending it is fun,
PE comes around, will people see them?
Home time close, home time near,
I can feel the end, the end is near.

Sahib Kanda (13)
Altrincham College Of Arts, Timperley

31

Immigration

Impacts lives can't you see?
Madness, it's in the news every week,
They are Mistaken for bad people,
It is unfaIr, we are all equal!
It is tirinG, we should just let them in,
Why aRe standards different?
We are all equAl, no matter where we are from,
Truly, we should be a team,
Don't be so Insensitive, we can all win,
BOrders should be open,
No Non-natives? You've got to be joking!

Oliver Gornall (13)
Altrincham College Of Arts, Timperley

Wrongly Convicted

Today's another day in his cell,
Today's another day I smell his smell,
Today's another day when I eat his food,
Today's another day I take his beatings,
Today's another day I serve his time,
Today's another day I lose my life.

Today's another day he takes my family,
Today's another day he takes my property,
Today's another day he takes my food,
Today's another day he smells my smells,
Today's another day he lives my life,
Today's another day he takes my friends,
Today's another day my life ends.

Myers James John Thornhill (11)
Altrincham College Of Arts, Timperley

Soldier, Soldier What Do You See?

An orphaned child, so young, so defeated,
Guns singing in unison in a war so heated.

Villagers shaken by the frequent *bang!*
So slick with red was the land.

Lifeless bodies dotted all around
As their eternal souls watch the battleground.

You wouldn't care with your money, with your wealth,
As slimming children beg for their health.

A living nightmare, they never want to awake,
Brutal warlords mocking their state.

A premature demise will be their fates,
What do you care? You wouldn't help them escape...

Juri Sammour (13)
Altrincham College Of Arts, Timperley

School

School is a drool,
With the teachers screaming at you for no reason,
Like they want to get you in jail for treason,
With disgusting food
And that one kid that says, "Dude!"
With PE teachers that think they're amazing,
But, really, they can't do anything,
Waking up early for a pile of *beep*,
Whilst I was deep in sleep,
I don't want to work,
Neither do I want to be a jerk,
But, I don't see how this helps,
So, if I could, I would drop out of school,
Because, honestly, school is a drool.

Luca Scholes-Drumm (13)
Altrincham College Of Arts, Timperley

Bullying Hurts So Bad!

B ullying hurts,

U s children try so hard to avoid bullying,

L et me help, children,

L et me help children around the world,

Y ou might not be hurt, but you might get it,

I don't like bullying, do you?

N obody should be mean to you,

G o and tell everybody!

H urts so bad, then come and tell me,

U s humans should not be animals,

R eally,

T ell me and I would make you feel good again,

S o, be kind and helpful.

Lydia Rose Macauley (11)
Altrincham College Of Arts, Timperley

The Earth

I cry like a kid because of you,
Because of you, you people, polluting me,
Breaking my heart because
You are destroying my beautiful and best friends,
I can hardly breathe because of your factories,
You are destroying your own homeland,
I feel like a prisoner,
You may not feel the pain but I can,
I see my friends being cut down
To make people their papers,
I know one day will come
When you people will stop doing this,
I may not have heaven on me,
But I do have pieces of it.

Fatima Iftikhar (11)
Altrincham College Of Arts, Timperley

What I See

Scared, homeless and alone,
I walk through the daunting wilderness,
All I see around me is neglect.

More forest fires,
Less food,
Living off dead branches and twigs.

It's not Mother Nature doing this,
It's men destroying this land,
I've lost all my home to those house builders.

I can hear them hunting me at night,
All alone in this destroyed land,
I'm getting pushed closer and closer to the lion's den,
They can smell me and I can smell them.

Molly-Jane Tomlinson (14)
Altrincham College Of Arts, Timperley

The World Today

It all started with the industrial revolution,
Where factories took place,
Though there is no solution,
Next is outer space.

Then, here come cars,
Their carbon monoxide in the air,
Our world will look like Mars,
But nobody cares.

Next come oil rigs,
They'll go as quickly as they came,
When the problem is big,
We'll find something that's the same.

On its way is fracking,
Earthquakes everywhere,
Safety is what is lacking,
But nobody cares.

Yousif Nasser (13)
Altrincham College Of Arts, Timperley

You Can't Accept The Truth

People can't understand what the truth is,
People can't understand what the truth means,
Nothing is how it seems.

Everyone says, "Let's save our planet!"
But most people don't do anything,
The animals that are dying aren't acting.

They think that they can't make a change by themself,
But, in real life, they just care about wealth.
I know I'm young but I just want people to listen,
So, in the future, our world will glisten.

Poppy Whillans
Altrincham College Of Arts, Timperley

Friends Are Not Trustworthy

Friends, friends,
They might look trustworthy,
But they are not.

Their faces will be full of
Slithering fakeness,
Their faces that you see
May look like diamonds
But they're plastic.

Some friends are diamonds,
Some friends are plastic,
They accuse you,
They lie.

Some friendship bonds are really weak,
These days, they embarrass you,
They bully you,
Friends are not heroes,
But some are.

Sohail Muhammad Safdar (12)
Altrincham College Of Arts, Timperley

The End Of The Ice Age

I'm strolling around,
No idea where I'm going,
On the snow-covered ground
And it is still snowing.

The ice is starting to disappear,
Icebergs are starting to fall,
The end is now near,
Now there are no seals to maul.

I am very sad and
I am filled with rage,
It's as if I'm hanging from a strand,
My life is starting to change.

It is the end of the Ice Age!

Ben Mather (13), Nathaniel & Adam
Altrincham College Of Arts, Timperley

Extinction Is Death

Death, it terrorises all animals,
It makes us all suffer,
Cold, it takes animals lives every day,
It makes us freeze or suffer,
Pollution drowns our lives in misery,
Makes us suffocate in smog,
Poaching slaughters animals day by day,
We use their skin as their children starve,
We stand here, on our own two feet
As the defenceless animals beg for mercy, but we keep on going,
We never stop, extinction, extinction is death.

Oliver Teggart (13) & Sam David Todd (13)
Altrincham College Of Arts, Timperley

My Hero

Truth is, I still miss my dad,
I miss playing football with him,
I miss how he would sing to me at bedtime.

He was my inspiration and still is,
He inspired me to play football,
This is when I feel closest to him.

He taught me to ride,
He taught me to fish,
He was patient and calm,
Nothing made him mad.

He was and he is my hero,
When I grow up, I want to be just like him.

Nicky Jacklin (13)
Altrincham College Of Arts, Timperley

The Grind

Every day, every night, I stream,
This is because I want to achieve my dream,
Or maybe the reality will never be seen.

I do YouTube, only get fifty views,
But, we all start somewhere to amuse,
Maybe one day, my channel can make the news.

People watch every move,
It's really important I do not lose,
One wrong move and the likes will stop,
I need to keep streaming to stay on top.

James Fogg (13)
Altrincham College Of Arts, Timperley

Like A Car

A person with peer pressure is like a car,
When told to, it works fine,
There are always bumps in the road
But it doesn't break.

A person is like a car because, sometimes,
It needs to be fixed when it is running out,
Whereas, other times, this car can't be fixed
And needs to be scrapped so,
We feel crushed, like a car in a junkyard,
The glass shatters like a person's soul.

Lucy Crawford (13)
Altrincham College Of Arts, Timperley

Mental Health

I am stuck in a prison, a prison of my own mind,
So many voices mocking me, haunting me and following me,
People say I have problems which I don't understand,
Depression throws me to a cold, dark place of my self-
esteem,
Insomnia pulls me into its arms away from sleep,
Can you escape from yourself?
No one understands the prison I am trapped in,
No one can help me from the prison in my mind.

Cy Kinnersley (13)
Altrincham College Of Arts, Timperley

Donald Trump's Evilness

Why should I care?
People say I am not fair,
I put children in cages
Down through ages,
I, Donald Trump,
Once jumped over a lump,
Everyone started laughing
When I was passing,
I will throw them in cages
Down through ages,
Then they will learn
That I don't just earn,
I put people in cages
Only if there are evil,
I am the best
In the West.

Alizah Syeda (11)
Altrincham College Of Arts, Timperley

The Future

The future is an amazing thing
But you will need to bring
Everything you have learnt at school
To get the job you choose,
A footballer, a vet,
I bet,
Just remember to be happy,
Get the job of your dreams,
Even if it's a builder building metal beams,
Once you get older and look at the past,
You can say,
"I had a blast!"

Gabriel Paul Ludden (13)

Altrincham College Of Arts, Timperley

Trapped

I'm trapped in the body of people of mine,
People say there is no need to hide
But I still feel dead inside,
I am the person in the corner
That no one will ever notice cower
And I have no power,
He is always in, shutting down my body,
I don't know what to do
So I will go back and hide.

Oliver Hillier (13)
Altrincham College Of Arts, Timperley

Donald Trump's Table

I was bought and put on a train,
Now I'm used to hold champagne,
I have to listen to him
Take the Lord's name in vain
And give others pain,
It really is such a shame,
In the newspaper,
His name is fame,
But really, he is plain,
So people give him pain.

Thomas Stait (11)
Altrincham College Of Arts, Timperley

Doctor

"Doctor, if you may,
You save lives every day,
My son is very sick,
You are not stupid, you are not thick,"
As he shuts the door,
I'm not sure,
Did I do something wrong for you to ignore?
"Help me, help my family, we are very poor."

Thomas James Marsland (13)
Altrincham College Of Arts, Timperley

The Awful Class

Here I am, back at this horrible school,
Where most children don't play by the rules,
Why do I have to deal with this class?
I just wish they would never push past,
A pounding headache,
A sore throat
And it is not even my fault,
They are truly an awful class.

Erin Lally (11)
Altrincham College Of Arts, Timperley

No Remedy For The Streets

I mean, he was like a brother to me,
He was a very close friend,
We would always go out together
And the teasing would never end.
I still have possession of his Jordan's '03 hat,
Blood stains all over like a thorn left in a rat.

Denzel, a brown-skinned boy,
Was always being stopped and approached,
Mind you, that was only because of his race,
It's not a topic I like to sugarcoat,
So I'm not even going to touch base,
He was just a typical teenager
Who would shoot hoops
And his scoreboard would never lack.

Gang-affiliated, he was not,
Well, the po-po just assumed that
'Cause the streets were hot,
One time, a couple of guys pulled up,
They backed out,
Knives, machetes and guns were struck.

I shuddered and screamed,
"Denzel, bro, quickstep for your life!"
I wept in the blackened boulevard
Because his body was a corpse on the street side,

When I realised I could no longer feel his heartbeat,
My body turned numb.

999, their confidential lines were bust,
So my only resort was a knife crime trust,
Keyword, trust.

From time to time, I mourn,
But this death is not going to leave me shattered nor torn,
I put him inside the grave, a feeling of déjà vu,
Oh, his jokes I will always crave,
In Loving Memory of Denzel,
(I can't bait out his government name,)
The funeral pamphlet read,
These lingering aches are the only things
I need strength to shed.

Chidera Melie
ARK All Saints Academy, Camberwell

My Thoughts

It's long to deal with oppression,
Always having to loathe my reflection,
People always knocking me down a step
When I'm trying to do my best,
The world is a dark place,
Wear a mask to hide my crying face,
Have you ever seen me cry?
If you ask if I'm fine, I really just lie,
I'm hurting inside,
Body left broken,
While I look at this cliff,
While I look at the scars on my wrist,
It's not only physical pain,
A psychological pain,
Feel like I'm going insane,
Trying to numb myself with pills and potions,
Guess you didn't know I was drowning in this ocean,
This cold place is where I feel safe,
This dark place is my grave.

Toluwalashe Ayoade
ARK All Saints Academy, Camberwell

Demons

Hiding in the dark,
On the swings in the park,
Listening to your dog bark,
Hunting like a shark,
As they lurk around
There's nothing to be found
Until you show fear,
They wouldn't shed a tear,
They showed no mercy for Percy,
So, now, it's your turn
To burn.

Chelsea Reed-Martin
ARK All Saints Academy, Camberwell

Thirteen

Lonely, so lonely
As I wandered throughout a space
Where are they?
Lonely so lonely.

I have lost many battles,
Lost many people,
That's a risk if you step
Into my ship.

I have lived with many faces
I am another version of Death.
Many people ask about my past,
But I am as silent as the grave.

I am another species and
My two hearts beat as one.
I may look alive
But it is not a life.

However, my vessel is my family
She keeps me going.
My refuge and
It is home which means I'm not alone...

Who am I? The Doctor.

Thomas Tuck (12)
Cantonian High School, Llandaff

Another Endless Night

She peered into the mirror too scared to see what stood
before her,
Her body a fragile bone structure,
Thoughts of hatred rushed around her toxic mind,
The dark started to crawl back in, consuming her again,
The blanket of lies suffocating, making it hard to breathe,
This was going to be another endless night,
She was her own worst enemy, criticising every little detail,
Her eyes too small, her body not perfect enough,
Why did she not look like everybody else?
Starving herself - her arms and legs as thin as toothpicks,
Her head determined, there was no talking to her,
She would stop at nothing to achieve perfection,
Her family were concerned, her friends worried,
She was on a slippery, spiralling slope,
Would she go too far?
Inside a broken, insecure, vulnerable girl
Silently screaming out for someone to rescue her,
A sea of sadness washed over her,
Breaking her down into a river of tears,
Perfection was so close, yet so far.

Juana-Mai Millar (16)
Coleraine Grammar School, Coleraine

Unfortunate Animals

Hello there, I'm just a regular cow,
You may be wondering, where am I now?
I could be at an auction or down the vets,
Perhaps I've been lured deep, drastically down into the unknown,
An ominous feeling attached and lingering with an unfamiliar tone,
The dreadful feeling, spreading like a parasite through my bones,
As I drown in a sea of grief,
Knowing my children are being cruelly snatched away and exposed to trauma,
You monsters sprint to the nearest shop to devour traces of my friends,
Whether it be a glass of milk or a slice of cheese,
Don't think of your calcium intake, think of me!
Think of the chickens, the pigs and the turkeys,
Their lives summarised between two pieces of wholemeal bread,
My mouth is twisted into an exclamation mark,
My eyes injected with panic,
My heart overthrown with anxiety, hysteria and constant agitation,
As your father returns from 'bringing home the bacon',
The furious animal lovers aim to help
But I believe this treadmill of terror and torture will never end,

You don't care, you don't see me,
Instead, you would rather eat,
Forever classing yourself as superior,
While the fruit hangs dreamily among the trees,
My question is, why gobble me?

Emily Kelly (15)
Coleraine Grammar School, Coleraine

The Prisoner

Prisoners in our own home, caged in our attic,
We were slaves to the regime,
My daughter, Anne, a symbol of strength,
Her suffering emerged the strongest of souls.

Flicking through the pages of her mind,
Every thought, an expression of her courage,
Her mind was a library of thoughts,
A world away from the eternal Nazi darkness.

She was a silent lion in our attic, with a heart of bravery,
Her innocent words fought the endless hatred,
Hunted like animals in the wild, we sat as quiet as mice,
But, yet, my daughter Anne was the rock of the family.

Her diary was her sword of truth,
Her friend Kitty an escape from the Nazi nightmare,
A friend in the world of words, a symbol of hope,
Holding all the secrets from our suffering.

Her heart, so pure and innocent,
With each word, an echo of beauty,
Every day, hour and minute, our fears grew,
No means of escape, the hunter was in pursuit of fresh prey.

Sarah Cromie (16)
Coleraine Grammar School, Coleraine

The Climb

Our tired bodies, laden with supplies,
Climbing higher, the end in sight,
The joyous mood to succeed,
Our bodies driven by adrenaline,
We didn't let the dark clouds dampen our determination to
reach the end,
But, then,
Disaster struck!

His friend's body, lifeless,
No breath of air he took,
Inside the cold, dark and stony coffin, there he laid,
His lips as dry as the Sahara desert, his skin was grazed and
bloody,
His eyes?
They looked heavenward to see a chink of light.

The rescue team came to the plight we were in,
There was no hope for my friend,
His spirit lived on,
Off to the summit we set
Even though our eyes wept.

Amy McCollum (15)
Coleraine Grammar School, Coleraine

The Feeling I Can't Seem To Escape From

Fighting back the tears in my eyes,
Trying to convince everyone I'm fine,
So worn down by my own thoughts,
Exhausted by my own despair to act normal,
Over-analyzing the past,
Trying not to stress about my future,
But, I can't stop,
Wishing I didn't have to feel like this,
Crying out, *why me?*
I'm now a master of concealing my thoughts and feelings from people,
Holding everything in, pretending to myself that I am okay,
This pain, invisible to us all, is slowly killing me,
The feeling, it will blind you,
Making you not see what matters clearly,
You feel so numb from the constant pins and needles,
What a sinister thing the mind can do to you.

Caitlin McCallan-McKendry (15)

Coleraine Grammar School, Coleraine

Kim Jong-Un (A Soldier's Point Of View)

Kim Jong-un, leader of North Korea? How you ask,
I don't know either.

From all of us in North Korea, we would like
To know how good your food is.

Vile, spiteful and obnoxious
Are some of the many words
I would use to describe you.

You have lots of money
But cannot provide for the poor,
I am sure you would rather be spending it
Planning a war.

You are not a great leader,
You are a great dictator,
You limit the freedom and speech of your people.

You demand respect without earning it.

Do you sleep in your bed at night,
Or, like me, do you lie in bed at night,
Fearing the future?

Jessica Dunlop (14)
Coleraine Grammar School, Coleraine

Coming Home From War

I remember the day that he came home,
Still not understanding why he had to go,
The waiting room filled with hopeful eyes,
Glistening like fireflies,
Mixed emotions had filled the air
And then we saw them standing there,
The silhouettes of our heroes,
A plague of smiles infected the room,
I ran up to him as he came through,
He grasped me tight like he'd never let go,
With a painted smile on his brave face I'd known,
Hiding the tragedies that left him scarred,
He will always be my star,
Not giving us any reason to worry,
But, one day, I hope to hear the true story.

Kiana Walker (15)
Coleraine Grammar School, Coleraine

Am I Really A Hero?

Am I really a hero if I kill?
If I march and sing but murder still?
The feeling of pain to fire my gun,
The reality that a war is never won,
The people chant and rejoice in praise,
But, they don't realise the price I've paid,
The feeling of anxiety, rage and fear,
Always thinking the enemy is near,
The constant flashback of comrades slaughtered,
My screaming and shouting scaring my daughter,
The pain and sadness I constantly feel,
The night tremors that feel so real,
Because of all this, I ask you still,
Am I really a hero if I kill?

Nathan Ogborne (15)
Coleraine Grammar School, Coleraine

Trapped

As if under twenty feet of cement,
I shout but no one hears.
So many messages trying to be sent,
But I have no one to wipe my tears.

I look at myself, doing things I don't want done,
I regret ever letting this person win.
I try to jump up but I weigh a ton,
As I try and not look at my skin.

I can see it ever so clearly, I don't want to push them away,
But that is when she starts to play.
I try and find a way to win, so I stay,
But if I try, she'll make sure that I don't see the next day.

Ruby Parkinson (14)
Coleraine Grammar School, Coleraine

Dump Trump

As I stand gloomily in front of Trump Tower,
I realise his extravagant power,
How can he be president?
His hair, a monstrosity
And his tan, an auburn traffic light,
Signalling a warning,
If he isn't boasting his name
In front of people,
He's building a wall,
Some say he's the star in the stripes
And call out, "Let's make America great again!"
However, time is ticking
Before we dump Trump
And really make America great again.

Charlotte Catherine McMullan (15)
Coleraine Grammar School, Coleraine

The Guy From Caffè Nero

Who would you describe as your hero?
Maybe like me, the worker at Caffè Nero,
He gives me my morning boost,
With the coffee that he produced,
He always wears a welcoming smile
When I come in from running my mile,
He doesn't get paid enough
For displaying out of this world cream puffs,
Cappuccino, flat white to even tea, he serves it all,
Though, I don't even know his name to call,
He's the first face I see
And the only person I want to be.

Georgie McLenaghan (15)
Coleraine Grammar School, Coleraine

A Day At The Beach

As the sun rose in the morning sky,
The sand warmed to the idea of a bright day ahead,
The shells paid tribute to the forgone neighbours,
The tormenting waves lulled by the rocking dinghy
On the rippling sea,
She clung to her teddy on her mother's knee,
Whispered prayers through coughs and the spray of the salty sea,
The strengthening, cresting waves that showed no mercy,
They found her there, face down in the sand,
The nation aghast, briefly.

Susan Green (15)
Coleraine Grammar School, Coleraine

My Bed

"My love!"
She yells again,
I pretend I'm deaf,
"Get up!" she shouts, going horse,
Cocooned in my duvet,
I am not ready to face the day ahead,
She bellows, "Now, shower!"
I stir and grunt in hopes of appeasing her,
What feels like hours for me,
Is nano-seconds for her,
I hear those dreaded words,
"Release the monster!"
Now, the battle begins,
The fight for my love,
Today I lose my love, my bed.

Marshall Neill (16)
Coleraine Grammar School, Coleraine

Ducky Darling

Splish, splash, splosh,
The fluffy bubbles getting even bigger,
The water swirling in ever-increasing circles.

Oh no! A tidal wave incoming!
The baby swirling and twirling into the whirlpool,
Heart racing, my mind chasing the dark thoughts,
Mum to the rescue as I pull the bath plug to drain the water.

What on Earth was I thinking and panicking about,
It is only my baby's yellow rubber duck!

Rachel McCollum (14)
Coleraine Grammar School, Coleraine

Strong

My heart was thumping in my chest,
My head spinning like a roundabout,
My leaden limbs frozen,
Trapped in my own mind,
My lungs craving oxygen
That my mouth could not provide,
Shivering, shaking, scared,
A prisoner of my body,
Conceal it inside,
Don't let anyone see,
They can't see that I'm not strong,
It will all be over soon,
Don't panic,
You are strong,
I believe in you.

Ella Stewart (14)
Coleraine Grammar School, Coleraine

The Pizza Poem

Some love it, some hate it,
But most can't beat it,
Comes in all shapes and sizes
As many toppings as you like.

Sometimes at a hefty price,
In my opinion, it's very nice,
Dominoes is hard to beat,
The pizza there is very neat.

Thin, crispy, round and flat,
Too much pizza will make you fat,
When it comes to your door, you'll hear a few knocks
And you'll see it's in a square box.

Luke Walton (14)
Coleraine Grammar School, Coleraine

Difficult Donald

An orange and enormous figure,
Yellow hair like an electrocuted canary,
His fight, strong,
His hair game, not so much.

A controversial and narcissistic man,
Although we fear he has a plan,
Build a wall! Build a wall!
But, which will be the first to fall?

Rebuilding, remodelling, repeat...
Not Trump Tower,
But, his ego, never discreet,
Difficult Donald in the president's seat.

Harry Hunter Hughes (15)
Coleraine Grammar School, Coleraine

The Truth Is Nothing But A Secret

When the truth is out and open,
Nothing can be spared,
Your deep and dreaded secrets
Are no longer yours to share.

Every waiting minute,
Anxious and afraid,
The problem is inflating,
No matter how long you wait.

The secrets have come to haunt me,
Like creatures in the dark,
Not knowing what they might do
Is definitely lighting up a spark.

Evie Scott (13)
Coleraine Grammar School, Coleraine

Supreme Leader

I'm Supreme Leader Kim Jong-un,
Spending millions on toys that go *boom!*
Even though my entire nation's in poverty,
I'm still buying Lambos as a novelty.

I made my country believe in unicorns
By dressing up horses with plastic horns.
All my people think I'm a god,
When I'm seen by my nation, they all applaud.

Charlie Orr (14)
Coleraine Grammar School, Coleraine

Baby Stormi

Kardashians all around me,
Barely with me,
I know they love me,
Outfits, eyelashes, surgery everywhere,
My mum wears fake hair,
Made billions from make-up,
Only cos she keeps putting her prices up,
My family helped with the environment,
I mean, they are clearly filled with plastic,
They look so drastic.

Charlotte Lynn (15)
Coleraine Grammar School, Coleraine

Trump

My tan went wrong last night,
My hair, what a wonderful sight!
I'm ready for the Mexicans to build my wall,
My great empire will never fall.

My botox does some wonders
And my wife's forty years younger,
Some may say she's a golddigger
But, oh my, what a wonderful figure.

Natasha Hamilton (14)
Coleraine Grammar School, Coleraine

Lies Or Truth?

The world is full of lies
Wherever we look or go,
I wish people would always tell the truth,
Then everyone would know.

Did someone cheat at this or that?
Is everything as it seems?
I don't think it will ever be 'all truth',
Except in all my dreams.

Toby McAuley (13)
Coleraine Grammar School, Coleraine

Chocolate, Through The Eyes Of A Fat Man

The chocolate is delicious, smooth and deep
But he has promises to keep,
After cake and lots of sleep,
Sweet dreams come to him cheap,
Once he wakes
He is left with a scare,
That chocolate which was once so yummy,
Has left him with a belly so chubby.

Kenzi Glass (16)
Coleraine Grammar School, Coleraine

Vision Of A Dog

I gasped when I saw those tears,
She screamed with a fright,
When the cold, dark night
Turning into light,
She cried with fright.

I licked her hands,
I licked her eyes,
She didn't calm down.

Her mum barged in,
She shouted and screamed,
Her tears were full with fears,
Her ears were bleeding
From all the noise.

Her room was a mess,
Her mum's fault,
I didn't know why she...
Why she touched her face like that.

My friend was shaking with fear,
But my little brain didn't understand why,
Why she screamed,
Why she cried,
All I remember is I turned outside
Into the freezing night.

Deimante Jonikaviciute (12)
Smestow School, Castlecroft

The Ancient Oak Tree

I never knew the teens were so bad,
Their species cut down my mum and dad,
They hang off my branches like I'm some sort of toy,
But what did I do to them?

If only I had legs to run away,
But, sadly, I'm here to stay,
They kick my roots, pick at my leaves
And stick gum all over me,
But what did I do to them?

Just ten minutes until third period ends
Just one more kick until my body bends,
I'll snap in half if this carries on,
But what did I do to them?

These grand old roots have seen a lot,
For now, on the inside, I'm starting to rot,
Now, my time has come to die,
I did nothing to them.

Abigail Bate (12)
Smestow School, Castlecroft

Cuba

We are here in Cuba,
I can hear the birds chirping,
I can see the palm trees swiftly moving side to side.

The bright sunset glowing in my face,
The fresh-squeezed orange juice,
The sounds of the calming waves,
Brings your mind to rest
When you are there.

Amelia Shokar (12)
Smestow School, Castlecroft

The Snow Leopard

White as snow,
Eyes of woe,
This is coming to an end
For me and my friend.

My habitat has been taken away
By other animals who eat my prey,
Nowhere to roam,
I've lost my home.

Through human's greed,
I am in need.

Ella Smith (12)
Smestow School, Castlecroft

Journey Of A Snowman

As the scintillating, sparkling snowflakes fall from the sky,
The excited, ecstatic children come running like cheetahs outside,
Joyful, jolly and full of laughter
And their smiles were massively wide.

Started as a handful of snow and gradually increased in size
And I began to develop and improve,
They gave me a mouth, eyes and a carrot as a nose
And, as they gave me stick arms, I discovered I couldn't move.

Whilst I watch them throw chilly, chalky snowballs at each other,
I wanted nothing more than to experience some of this fun,
But, as the piercing weather began to worsen,
The shivering, sleepy children decided that they were done,
So, there I stood, left isolated and lonely,
Knowing that, soon enough, I'd melt away,
Then, the blaring sunlight gazed down on me
And, as water dripped, I knew that this could be my last day.

As more and more water slowly transformed into a puddle,
The smaller I became and hotter became the sun,
I think this is the end, I know this is the end,
This is where all you did will be undone.

Natasha Taylor (12)
The Wigston Academies Trust, Wigston

Nod Of Approval

Matchday! Time to get up,
I've only got five to make a coffee,
So, as he stomps down the stairs,
Hell begins!

It's funny how time flies,
By his manager's side, 10:30 on the dot,
To wake him up,
Throwing him in the shower's what we try.

Getting his kit on didn't take much time,
But now I had to try and get his boots on,
I had to rush because I'd soon be standing on the sidelines,
In agony, I forced them on.

We're running late, scrambling him in the car,
I'm giving him the 'pre-match pep talk',
We're playing at home, so it's not that far,
"Them kicks need to be on point!"

We've arrived at the ground,
We're playing at home,
There's no one in navy when I look around,
So, we just play on my phone.

The boys are starting to rock up,
So I usher him out of the car,
"I'll meet you down there,
I'm not watching the warm-up!"

As I take my position on the pitch near his net,
Matty's dad tells me,
"Your lad's going to have a lot to do, I bet!"
So, as the ref blows his whistle,
I give him the signature nod of approval.

Cameron Lee (12)
The Wigston Academies Trust, Wigston

A Busy Day

Packed my bags,
Ready to leave,
Spilt some juice up my sleeve,
Got in the car,
Parents shout, blah, blah, blah,
Seat belts on, ready to go,
Suddenly, I shout, "No!"
Get my phone,
Click a snap.
Put it on my story on Snapchat!

Halfway through the journey,
Luckily I packed some money,
Go to the airport,
Ate some food,
Then I ended up spending my money on juice,
Gave in our suitcases,
Ready to leave,
My sister was acting very mean,
I slapped her across the face,
A lady pulled up a case.

She was dressed smart,
Even though she was about to start
Blabbering on to my parents,
I pulled Mum's hand,

There were only ten minutes left
Until the plane went.

We ran for our lives before it could leave
Until I realised the juice was still up my sleeve,
I didn't care,
Unless I had nice hair,
Finally sat on our seats on the plane,
A kid in front was acting like he was on a train,
He sang for at least twenty minutes,
The air hostess gave us a tin
Filled with colours and crayons,
Packed with paper,
Sat and relaxed,
We finally go to our journey at last.

Harsimran Sadhra (12)
The Wigston Academies Trust, Wigston

Sea Turtle

I'm scared, I don't know what to do,
My family is dying and it's all because of you.
There are tears in my eyes that weren't there before,
By the way this is going, there will be another war.
My time is ending, I don't have long to live,
You're using too much plastic, why are you doing this?
When I was younger, my home was bright blue,
There used to be a lot of us, now there's only a few.
There is so much plastic, I'm really confused,
Why don't you just recycle and reuse?

My family, the leatherbacks, greens and loggerheads,
They're slowly leaving me, most of them are dead.
Global warming, pollution and plastic debris,
Entanglement and rubbish are all I can see.
Before, I longed to always be in the sea,
Now I wish I could just get away and flee.
If you don't stop, my home will be gone,
But I must have hope, I'll try to carry on.
My nightmares are real, they're coming alive,
Please help me, I'm just trying to survive.

Freya Mistry (13)
The Wigston Academies Trust, Wigston

Dogs

I was a dog called Jessy,
I was very messy,
I chewed the wall instead of the ball,
I'm a little staff that made Alyssa laugh,
I loved to play but couldn't stay,
So in the end, they gave me away.

Oscar is my name,
I liked to play some games
Until I got bored and thought it was lame,
So, I sucked on my bear and took it everywhere,
I am small like Alyssa, but buff,
When it comes to food, I've had enough.

Buddy is my name,
I love to play some games
Until it's time to eat, my record cannot be beaten,
I'm lanky for my breed and have lots of speed,
I love it when my owner sings,
Especially when it's about me!

Thanks for listening about my pooches,
I will definitely give them smooches
And give them a big cuddle
For not getting in a lot of trouble,
I love them all and dogs overall.

Alyssa Eve Vaja (12)
The Wigston Academies Trust, Wigston

Equality Over Power!

No matter what people say,
They bring you down,
They toss you away,
Don't listen, fight back,
We are all humans at the end of the day.

Just because you're a woman, doesn't mean
You're less capable than a man,
You're less powerful than a man,
You're less intelligent than a man,
Or you're less anything than a man.

No matter what gender you are,
No matter what colour you are,
That doesn't mean you are any better,
Or even any worse than anyone,
We are all the same,
We are all equal in this world.

This isn't just one person's home,
This is everyone's home,
We have to fight for our home,
At the end of the day
We are all unique in every single way,
Don't let anyone tell you otherwise.

Stand up for what is right,
Not for what is easy,

Don't give up a fight,
They've thrown the first punch,
It's time for us to finish it!

Marissa Faye McFarlane (12)

The Wigston Academies Trust, Wigston

Through Their Eyes

Through her eyes, I see the pain,
The hurtful words and all the mind games,
Far beyond those bright blue eyes,
I see all the tears that she had once cried.

The worry, the doubt, the pressure to please,
Though isolation is all that she sees,
Snapchat, Instagram, TV and boys
Just make her feel like old, used toys.

The hatred she has when she looks in the mirror
And the disgust she feels when she sees her own figure,
The lies, the girls and the guys don't help,
They all just add to the pain she has felt.

She's only thirteen,
Living the 'teenage dream',
"Oh, why?" she cries,
"Oh, why has it happened to me?"

Raegan Hamp (12)
The Wigston Academies Trust, Wigston

Toys On The Shelf

Sitting here with endless hope,
Trying not to make a move,
Waiting around, surrounded by kids,
My game needs to improve.

I can't talk or speak,
Make any sudden sounds,
I'm determined to escape
But everywhere's out of bounds.

The plastic on me is getting heavy,
I would just like to get out,
Being a human must be amazing,
Actually being able to shout.

From January to December,
I'm here all day,
From dusk 'til dawn,
Kept out the way.

Hanging around with nothing to do,
Silent without a mate,
Being a toy on the shelf,
It really isn't great.

Lottie Parnham (12)
The Wigston Academies Trust, Wigston

A New Day

As his veins pump through the body,
He wakes up in a new day,
The birds are tweeting in the air,
Morning music is playing peacefully.

As he jumps out of his warm bed,
His carpet ready to be jumped on,
He walks to his kitchen to make his breakfast,
The sun beams through the glass.

Ready to get dressed for school,
He puts on his school uniform
And walks to his beloved school,
The bell rings, signalling the children to go to class.

Time goes through the sun,
Then, the last bell rings,
The last day of school,
Everyone runs home for a good night's sleep.

Lukas Peikstenis (11)
The Wigston Academies Trust, Wigston

Banksy

As I slide through the night,
Quietly spraying my can,
I try not to give anyone a fright,
If I ever got caught, I would certainly get a ban.

My name is Banksy,
If the rain thinks it can stop me,
It's acting madly,
I am the man, I tell myself,
I am not going to do this badly.

I am the unknown,
I try to keep myself on the low tone
And I never take my phone,
I always work alone
So that they don't moan.

My work is well-known art,
One of them is a tart,
Do I walk?
Do I talk?
Do I go by cart?
I am the unknown.

Myah Seager (11)
The Wigston Academies Trust, Wigston

Climate Change (Greta)

C hange - we need to change our habits,
L ive - we want our world to live longer,
I will make a change,
M ake the world a better place,
A im to help the planet,
T ake - we need to take action,
E veryone can make a change.

C an - we can save our planet,
H ave your say in what happens,
A lways think about what you could do to help,
N ever forget! We need to help,
G ive - never give up,
E very piece of plastic hurts the environment.

Ashleigh Silver (11)
The Wigston Academies Trust, Wigston

Donald Trump

We need to build a wall,
We need to build a wall,
We need to build a big, beautiful wall.

Now the wall is built,
Now the wall is built,
My big, beautiful wall.

It's 1000 metres tall,
It's 1000 metres tall,
Oh, my big, beautiful wall.

Actually, it's just metal,
Actually, it's just three metres tall,
Oh, my big, beautiful wall.

My little, metal wall,
Oh, my little, metal wall,
Now my mission is complete,
Now it is complete,
Now I have a perfect metal wall.

Mia Jennifer Berry (11)
The Wigston Academies Trust, Wigston

I Wonder

I wander through the halls all day,
Hoping they'll have something to say,
Maybe they'll see the pain in my eyes
And offer just a little, "Hi!"
Every day gets worse and worse,
Being invisible really does hurt,
This is when the thoughts will start,
I begin to feel an ache in my heart,
I wonder if they even care
And would they notice if I wasn't there?
This is when I'll rush around,
I need my blade, I need it now,
I need to escape this pain I feel,
I need a way for me to heal.

Theo Thomas Burrows (11)
The Wigston Academies Trust, Wigston

Waiting For Death

I sit in my cell, waiting for death,
Just waiting to take my last breath,
I'm not scared or worried,
I wish my death is hurried,
The way the victim's family thinks,
It's the thing that really stinks,
Arm for an arm,
Eye for an eye,
Sometimes I'll just wish I'd die,
I've got hours to go until I pass,
Until my brain turns to mash,
I think about life, all my mistakes,
I could have been all it takes,
But I'm just a demon,
A demon who kills innocent women.

Lily-Mae Jobling (12)
The Wigston Academies Trust, Wigston

Life Being A Teen

Being a teenager is sometimes hard,
School and social media, where do I start?
Always on Instagram twenty-four-seven,
Just wander to a life of your own
While people go to heaven.

Days go by like the wind through your hair,
You care about your size but not what you wear!
Mental health plays a part too,
Being skinny is a thing for teenagers but not for you.

So, this is what it's like being a teen,
All grumpy, all tired and a little mean!

Georgia Sylvester (12)
The Wigston Academies Trust, Wigston

Do You See Me?

Do you see me sitting here?
Thinking of yesteryear.

I hear your voice, I know your name,
Do you know mine, do you hear the same?

Times gone by, you will not know,
You do not know, I will not show.

I hear the voices of friends long gone,
I feel the pain, I know the wrong.

Do you know who I am?
Do you know what I can?

I hope what I have seen,
You don't see in me.

Do you see me sitting here?
I see you, do you see me?

Jamie Lakin (13)
The Wigston Academies Trust, Wigston

Insane Man

Through his eyes, I can see apple pies,
Through his eyes, I see a life of lies,
This is all his life,
Through his eyes, I see a lonely wife,
Sitting in shame with only him to blame,
This is his life, this is his life.

I see a man who's a criminal,
I see a man who's turning insane,
This is all his life,
This is all his life,
Through his eyes, I see a prison cell,
Through his eyes, I see a child in a well,
He's insane, he's insane.

Daniel Craven (11)
The Wigston Academies Trust, Wigston

It's A Dog's Life

I just can't wait for my owner, Simon, to get home,
We go on the best walks ever!
Sat there, impatiently, chewing on my bone,
We go for walks whatever the weather.

I just can't understand why he has to have a cup of tea
At exactly half-past three.

The lead comes out,
The wellies go on
And with a shout,
"Come on Tom!"

At the park, I sniff the conkers,
They smell like mud and squirrels,
All this makes me go bonkers!

Alex Exton (12)
The Wigston Academies Trust, Wigston

Tragedy

As I fight against this fear,
I wait in this bed
For Death to take me away,
I see my family's faces in tears
As I slowly disappear.

I can't see them suffer anymore,
Their faces white and bare,
Around me, medical equipment galore,
The doctors around me
Is all that I saw.

I now close my eyes one last time,
Now, up here in Heaven,
The peaceful bells will chime,
This tragedy, I am lost in time.

Emily Crouch (13) & Molly Hanney (13)
The Wigston Academies Trust, Wigston

A Poem About Bullying

Once a girl left school
Because all the people were cruel,
She wanted the bullying to end
But the bullies didn't stop,
Not only did the bullies not stop,
But they stuck notes on her desk
And treated her like a pest,
That was it!

Once a girl left school
Because all the people there were cruel,
She had no friends,
She wanted to bullying to end,
But the bullies didn't stop.

Cassie Birdas (11)
The Wigston Academies Trust, Wigston

James Maddison

Here we were,
Marching out the tunnel,
Ready to begin our new match,
We shook the opposition's hands
While Wes Morgan put on his captain band,
After that, we ran into our positions,
My mind was filled with ambitions,
We got kick-off,
My heart was racing,
My stomach was churning,
And, before I knew it
The match was up and running,
Here came my first tackle...

Lili Rutter (12)
The Wigston Academies Trust, Wigston

Batman In Gotham City

I tried hard to stop the crime,
To help Gotham City have a peaceful time,
But my enemies did their best
To put my skills to the test,
With rivals such as the Joker and Harley Quinn,
They really got under my skin,
As I was ready for the fight,
My enemies would disappear into the night,
I brought an end to evil and corruption,
Gotham City would prosper without interruption!

Mason Johnson (12)
The Wigston Academies Trust, Wigston

Martin Luther King

I had a dream
To make the world fair
For people everywhere.

I had a dream
To be free
No matter what my race may be.

I had a dream
To sit down with you
And not be treated like mud on your shoe.

I had a dream
To be treated not by the colour of my skin
But by my character within.

I had a dream...

Sara Filali (12)
The Wigston Academies Trust, Wigston

My First Escape

The prison yards are empty,
Not a crow in sight,
All the windows fully-lit
On this cold and windy night,
I try to escape from all this harm,
That's when I hear that evil alarm,
The sound is blaring through my ears,
I have to get right out of here,
Back to the prison cell for my crimes,
Maybe I'll try another time.

Faye Chloe Hincks (13)
The Wigston Academies Trust, Wigston

I Had A Dream

They all bow down to me.
A man of history,
Thanks to Rosa Parks
We're no longer left in the dark,
One small step for man,
One giant leap for humanity,
Although they sing my praise,
I'm left counting the days
Before I am but a memory,
As legends fall,
Stories live on,
I had a dream
That, one day, racism will be gone.

Milly Jade Shaw (12)
The Wigston Academies Trust, Wigston

Prison Life - Death Row

The cell doors bang,
I'm trapped,
Guards watching my every move,
Tasers at the ready,
Death row coming my way.

Handcuffed and trapped,
I must stand tall,
Walking through the halls,
Death row coming my way.

Eating my last meal,
Chained by the ankles,
Silence,
Death row coming my way...

Frances Mitchell (12)
The Wigston Academies Trust, Wigston

Mind Of A Prisoner

Jail is a nightmare come true,
Jail is a lonely dungeon,
Jail is waiting, waiting for you,
Jail is a torturer.

You're trying to figure out why you're here,
Its walls closing in,
Crushing, crushing the hope that, one day, you'll be free,
When you know you'll never truly be free,
Free from the pain you've caused.

Woody Orton (12)
The Wigston Academies Trust, Wigston

Through A Dog's Eyes

I lie in my bed
With a tear in my eye,
There's nobody home,
I just want to die.

But, then, they come home
And fill me with joy,
They give me my dinner
And I play with my toy.

We go for a walk
Through wind, rain and sleet,
When we get home,
They give me a treat!

Danny Beattie (12)
The Wigston Academies Trust, Wigston

Barnold The Tortoise

My legs are slow
But I'm not old,
I love the summer
But not the cold,
I eat no meat,
All plants for me.
The garden is rich
As far as I can see,
It doesn't bother me
That every day's the same,
I'll keep plodding along,
Barnold the tortoise is my name.

Oliver Bailey (12)
The Wigston Academies Trust, Wigston

To Be Me

I shivered, crying loudly,
I didn't know what to do,
My lips quivered,
My tears landed on my shoe,
"Who am I?" I said,
The tears kept falling,
The blood rushed to my head,
But, then I realised
Who I was destined to be,
Not perfect,
But to be me!

Anya Brown (11)
The Wigston Academies Trust, Wigston

Pineapple

Do people like me?
I think not,
Some people love me,
Some not,
Me on pizza?
Yes, okay!
Some say that it's not okay,
So, do people like me?
Yes or no?
Give me an answer,
I just want to know!

Hannah Vann (12)
The Wigston Academies Trust, Wigston

Screen

I see a hole,
The truth floods,
Lines of code,
Ones and zeros.

I realise the truth of this.

The screen is unclear,
Everything is static,
Everything is fake,
I am going insane.

Everything is controlled,
Everything is coded,
Life is a lie,
It doesn't have meaning.

I know the truth.

I can break free,
I'm not controlled by a script,
But, I shouldn't flee.

I need to make sure the others know
That this is a game,
But, if I tell them,
Our lives wouldn't be the same.

Everything in this world is a lie.

Tyler Anthony Shannon (11)
Walney School, Walney

I Thought He Liked Me...

He seemed nice,
He seemed like he loved me,
But I was wrong.

Every day, I get a bruise,
Every day, I feel small,
Every day, I feel...

If I go out, he criticises me,
Every outfit, I have to change,
I can't leave him,
I can't,
All my friends say I should...

He says he goes out with his guy friends,
I'm not that dumb.

I am covered in bruises.
I hurt.
I can't take anymore.

Phoebe Lovidge (14)
Walney School, Walney

Change

Too fat,
Too skinny,
Gain weight,
Lose weight.

Change.

Your ponytail's too low,
Your hair's too frizzy,
It's the wrong colour,
It's too short.

Change.

Too tall,
Too small,
Too immature,
Grow up,
Life's not a stage,
Act your age,
You're too childish,
Put away your toys,
Open a book.

Change.

Neve Fallon (14)
Walney School, Walney

YOUNG WRITERS
INFORMATION

We hope you have enjoyed reading this book – and that you will continue to in the coming years.

If you're a young writer who enjoys reading and creative writing, or the parent of an enthusiastic poet or story writer, do visit our website **www.youngwriters.co.uk**. Here you will find free competitions, workshops and games, as well as recommended reads, a poetry glossary and our blog. There's lots to keep budding writers motivated to write!

If you would like to order further copies of this book, or any of our other titles, then please give us a call or order via your online account.

Young Writers
Remus House
Coltsfoot Drive
Peterborough
PE2 9BF
(01733) 890066
info@youngwriters.co.uk

Join in the conversation!
Tips, news, giveaways and much more!

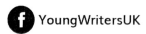 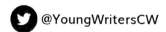